BY SUPPER POSSESSED

Charles M. Schulz

Panel 1: DO YOU KNOW WHY I'M LIMPING?

Panel 2: WHEN I WAS FIXING YOUR DINNER, I DROPPED THE CAN OF DOG FOOD ON MY FOOT!

Panel 3: I ALSO CUT MY FINGER ON THE CAN OPENER...

Panel 4: THIS WOULD BE A BAD TIME TO ASK FOR AN AFTER DINNER MINT

© 1986 United Feature Syndicate, Inc. 4-8

TOPPER BOOKS

AN IMPRINT OF PHAROS BOOKS • A SCRIPPS HOWARD COMPANY

NEW YORK

First published in 1988

PEANUTS Comic Strips: © 1986
United Feature Syndicate, Inc.

Cover Art: PEANUTS Characters © 1958, 1965
United Feature Syndicate, Inc.

Paperback edition distributed in the United States by
Ballantine Books, a division of Random House, Inc. and
in Canada by Random House of Canada, Ltd.

Library of Congress Catalog Card Number: 87-071944
Pharos ISBN: 0-88687-329-0
Ballantine Books ISBN: 0-345-35228-9

Printed in United States of America

Topper Books
An Imprint of Pharos Books
A Scripps Howard Company
200 Park Avenue
New York, NY 10166

10 9 8 7 6 5 4 3 2 1

DO YOU THINK YOU'RE A DIFFERENT PERSON FROM WHAT YOU WERE LAST YEAR?

DO YOU THINK YOU'VE REALLY CHANGED?

© 1985 United Feature Syndicate, Inc.

I REMEMBER LAST YEAR YOU SAID YOU WERE GOING TO TRY TO BE A BETTER LISTENER..

WHAT?

1-1-86

SCHULZ

THE MEETING OF THE TOBOGGAN CLUB WILL COME TO ORDER..

AS YOU KNOW, TONIGHT IS OUR TOBOGGAN PARTY... WE NEED A VOLUNTEER TO BRING A TUNA CASSEROLE..

1-2-86

GOOD.. WE'LL SEE YOU ALL TONIGHT

© 1985 United Feature Syndicate, Inc.

VERY FEW THINGS IN LIFE MAKE YOU FEEL MORE FOOLISH THAN SITTING ALONE ON A TOBOGGAN IN THE DESERT HOLDING A TUNA CASSEROLE!

SCHULZ

PEANUTS

featuring

"Good ol' CharlieBrown"

by SCHULZ

Poof!

Dear

I miss you more each day. I love you more than words can say.

1-3-86

THAT'S NICE, BUT WHO ARE YOU WRITING TO?

I CAN ALWAYS FILL THAT IN LATER..

OH, NO!

1-4-86

I HATE IT WHEN..

© 1985 United Feature Syndicate, Inc.

..A TUMBLEWEED GETS IN YOUR SLEEPING BAG!

DO YOU LIKE ME?

1-6-86

AS A PERSON?

OR AS A SISTER?

© 1985 United Feature Syndicate, Inc.

FORGET IT! I DON'T WANT TO HEAR THE REST!

SOMETIMES I GET LONELY...

1-7-86

SOMETIMES I WISH I HAD SOMEONE TO SNUGGLE UP TO....

© 1985 United Feature Syndicate, Inc.

I SURE CAN'T SNUGGLE UP TO A CACTUS..

TUMBLEWEEDS DON'T DO MUCH FOR ME, EITHER!

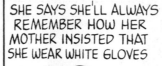
MY GRANDMOTHER SAYS HER FIRST DATE WAS AN EVENING AT THE OPERA...

SHE SAYS SHE'LL ALWAYS REMEMBER HOW HER MOTHER INSISTED THAT SHE WEAR WHITE GLOVES

HOW ABOUT HER DATE? WHO WAS THE BOY?

WHO KNOWS? ALL SHE REMEMBERS IS THE WHITE GLOVES!

1-8-86

© 1985 United Feature Syndicate, Inc.

DIGGING FOR RARE EGYPTIAN COINS CAN BE VERY EXCITING...

IF YOU FIND THE RIGHT ONES, YOU COULD MAKE A FORTUNE..

1-9-86 © 1985 United Feature Syndicate, Inc.

ALL IT TAKES IS FAITH AND PATIENCE

UNLESS, OF COURSE, IT SUDDENLY OCCURS TO YOU THAT YOU'RE IN THE WRONG DESERT..

PEANUTS
featuring
"*Good ol' CharlieBrown*"
by Schulz

OKAY.. LAST LETTER

"DEAR DR. SNOOPY... DRIVING HOME FROM WORK IN THE EVENING FIGHTING ALL THE TRAFFIC GETS ME VERY UPSET..."

"WHAT CAN I DO TO RELIEVE THIS STRESS?"

BEFORE YOU GET IN YOUR CAR, BUY YOURSELF AN ICE CREAM CONE...I'D SUGGEST CHOCOLATE ON THE TOP AND VANILLA ON THE BOTTOM...

NOW YOU WON'T MIND WAITING AT STOP SIGNS BECAUSE YOU CAN JUST SIT THERE AND LICK YOUR ICE CREAM CONE!

YOU MIGHT ALSO GET A DOG TO RIDE WITH YOU..IT WILL GIVE YOU SOMEONE TO TALK TO..DOGS ARE GOOD LISTENERS... YOU SHOULD ALSO BUY THE DOG AN ICE CREAM CONE...

1-12

INCIDENTALLY, DON'T TRY THIS WITH A CAT..CATS ARE POOR LISTENERS...

© 1986 United Feature Syndicate, Inc.

SLASH!

HE'S A POOR LISTENER, BUT HE HEARS EVERYTHING I SAY!

SCHULZ

I WONDER WHAT WOULD HAPPEN IF I ASKED THAT LITTLE RED-HAIRED GIRL IF I COULD SIT NEXT TO HER, AND EAT LUNCH...

MAYBE SHE'D TELL ME TO GET LOST, OR THROW A ROCK AT ME OR HIT ME WITH A STICK...

1-14

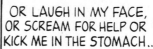

OR LAUGH IN MY FACE, OR SCREAM FOR HELP OR KICK ME IN THE STOMACH...

I WONDER IF SHE COULD DO ALL THOSE THINGS AT ONCE..

© 1986 United Feature Syndicate, Inc.

I'M TIRED OF BEING WISHY-WASHY! I'M GONNA WALK RIGHT OVER, AND TALK TO THAT LITTLE RED-HAIRED GIRL!

I'M DOING IT! I'M COMMITTED! NOTHING CAN STOP ME NOW!

© 1986 United Feature Syndicate, Inc.

ABSOLUTELY NOTHING!

1-15

WHAT WOULD HAPPEN IF YOU AND I NEVER GOT MARRIED AND LEFT HOME?

WHAT IF YOU AND I HAD TO LIVE TOGETHER FOR THE REST OF OUR LIVES?

1-16 © 1986 United Feature Syndicate, Inc.

DON'T SCARE ME LIKE THAT...IT'S TOO HARD ON MY HAIR!

A FINE DOG YOU ARE! I'LL BET YOU DON'T EVEN REMEMBER MY NAME!

1-17

MY INITIALS ARE C.B., AND MY FIRST NAME IS THE SAME AS THE FAMOUS ACTOR, CHAPLIN...

MY LAST NAME RHYMES WITH 'CROWN'

HINTS! I NEED MORE HINTS!

© 1986 United Feature Syndicate, Inc.

IT'S FUNNY HOW YOU CAN GO THROUGH LIFE THINKING YOU'VE SEEN EVERYTHING...

THEN, YOU SUDDENLY REALIZE THERE ARE MILLIONS OF THINGS YOU'VE NEVER SEEN BEFORE

NOBODY APPRECIATES HOW WISHY-WASHY PEOPLE SUFFER..

1-18

OUR LIVES ARE IN CONSTANT TORMENT

YOU KNOW WHAT WISHY-WASHY PEOPLE NEED?

© 1986 United Feature Syndicate, Inc.

CRINGE BENEFITS!

SCHULZ

"FUNDING FOR THIS PROGRAM WAS PROVIDED BY DONATIONS FROM OUR VIEWERS..."

1-20   © 1986 United Feature Syndicate, Inc.

"AND WASTED BY A PRODUCER WHO DIDN'T KNOW WHAT HE WAS DOING.."

SCHULZ

YES, MA'AM, I LEFT MY LUNCH BOX ON THE CURB BY THE BUS STOP...

1-23

SOMEONE'S PROBABLY FOUND IT BY NOW

I JUST HOPE WHOEVER FOUND IT APPRECIATES A GOOD LUNCH...

© 1986 United Feature Syndicate, Inc.

NO DOUGHNUTS !?!

SCHULZ

THIS IS MY REPORT ON THE "KILLER BEES"

MANY PEOPLE ARE WORRIED ABOUT THE "KILLER BEES"

1-24

© 1986 United Feature Syndicate, Inc.

NOT ME

WHAT I WORRY ABOUT ARE THOSE "KILLER D-MINUSES"!

SCHULZ

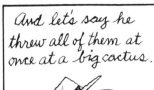

Dear National Geographic Society, Let's say a person had two-dozen marshmallows.

And let's say he threw all of them at once at a big cactus.

How many do you think would stick?

1-27 © 1986 United Feature Syndicate, Inc.

Are you interested in knowing?

THESE CATALOGS WITH THEIR MODELS ARE DEPRESSING! EVERYONE IS HANDSOME AND BEAUTIFUL!

LOOK AT THEM IN THEIR NEW SPRING CLOTHES...IT SETS AN IMPOSSIBLE STANDARD FOR US KIDS...

NONE OF US CAN EVER GROW UP TO LOOK THAT GOOD

1-28

I WILL!

PEANUTS

featuring

"Good ol' CharlieBrown"

by SCHULZ

WHEN WE DIE, WILL WE GO TO HEAVEN?

I LIKE TO THINK SO..

WHEN WE GET THERE, WILL WE MEET ALL THE BUGS WE'VE STEPPED ON?

WILL WE WHAT?

WILL WE MEET ALL THE SPIDERS, AND BUGS AND THINGS WE'VE STEPPED ON ALL OUR LIVES?

1-31

SOUNDS LIKE A TRAIN GOING THROUGH A TUNNEL, HUH, MA'AM?

SO HERE I AM AGAIN RIDING ON THE BACK OF MOM'S BICYCLE...

SHE HAS WHAT IS KNOWN AS A 10-SPEED..

YIPE!

ELEVEN, IF YOU COUNT SIDEWAYS!

2-1

2-2

ALL THE SNOW IN THIS PART OF THE YARD IS MINE.. THE SNOW IN THAT PART OF THE YARD IS YOURS..

1-25 © 1986 United Feature Syndicate, Inc.

I'VE BEEN WONDERING ABOUT SOMETHING...

LOOK I MADE THREE DOLLARS SHOVELING SIDEWALKS!

YOU'RE LUCKY WE LIVE WHERE IT SNOWS

YOU'RE RIGHT..I'VE OFTEN WONDERED WHAT IT WOULD BE LIKE TO LIVE WHERE IT DOESN'T SNOW...

2-3

SHOVEL YOUR WALK?

© 1986 United Feature Syndicate, Inc.

I'M GOING TO MAKE MY OWN VALENTINES THIS YEAR..

I'M GOING TO CUT OUT SOME PRETTY RED HEARTS, AND GLUE LACE AROUND THEM...

WHAT I WANT YOU TO DO IS TYPE OUT A NICE VERSE

Chocolate chip cookies are red.
Chocolate chip cookies are blue.
Chocolate chip cookies are sweet.
So are you.

THIS IS TERRIBLE! I CAN'T MAKE A VALENTINE WITH THAT! WRITE ANOTHER ONE!!

2-9

Angel food cake with seven-minute frosting is red...Angel food cake with seven-minute frosting is blue... Angel food cake with seven-minute frosting is sweet... So are you.

THAT'S THE DUMBEST THING I'VE EVER READ!

I GUESS I MISUNDERSTOOD... I THOUGHT SHE WANTED SOMETHING SENTIMENTAL..

SCHULZ

HERE'S THE WORLD WAR I FLYING ACE HIGH OVER NO MAN'S LAND...

I SUPPOSE YOU THINK YOU'RE FLYING OVER NO MAN'S LAND, HUH?

2-10

© 1986 United Feature Syndicate, Inc.

WELL, WHAT ABOUT NO WOMAN'S LAND?!

HERE'S THE WORLD WAR I FLYING ACE HIGH OVER NO PERSON'S LAND...

HERE'S THE LONELY WORLD WAR I FLYING ACE SITTING IN A SMALL FRENCH CAFE..

YOUR ROOT BEER, MONSIEUR

I'M IN LOVE! IT'S THE BEGINNING (SIGH) OF ANOTHER TRAGIC ROMANCE...

© 1986 United Feature Syndicate, Inc.

2-11

I'VE ONLY BEEN IN FRANCE FOUR HOURS, AND ALREADY I'VE HAD SEVEN TRAGIC ROMANCES!

YOUR NOSE IS WARM, MONSIEUR.. DO YOU FEEL ALL RIGHT?

HAVE YOU HEARD OF THE INFLUENZA EPIDEMIC? THEY SAY SIXTY-FIVE THOUSAND SOLDIERS AT CAMP PONTANEZEN, HERE IN FRANCE, HAVE THE FLU!

2-12

I THINK YOU HAVE A FEVER..

IT'S EITHER THE FLU OR LOVE..THE SYMPTOMS ARE THE SAME...

2-13

HORRORS, MONSIEUR!

YOU ARE GOING TO FLY EVEN THOUGH YOU ARE ILL WITH INFLUENZA?!

DUTY CALLS! THE WORLD WAR I FLYING ACE MUST CARRY ON!

UNLESS I COULD GET A NOTE FROM MY MOTHER..

© 1986 United Feature Syndicate, Inc.

YOU STILL HAVE A FEVER, MONSIEUR..YOU SHOULDN'T HAVE FLOWN YESTERDAY...

THE NEWS FROM THE FRONT IS STILL BAD... AND EVERYONE HAS THE FLU...

2-14

DO YOU THINK YOU COULD EAT SOMETHING? YOU NEED TO KEEP UP YOUR STRENGTH...

HOW ABOUT A BOWL OF DOG FOOD SOUP?

© 1986 United Feature Syndicate, Inc.

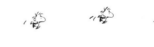

BONJOUR, MONSIEUR... HOW ARE YOU FEELING TODAY? I BROUGHT YOU A NEWSPAPER...

I THOUGHT YOU MIGHT LIKE TO HAVE ME READ TO YOU...THE WAR IS STILL GOING BADLY...

2-15

© 1986 United Feature Syndicate, Inc.

THE TROOPSHIP "LEVIATHAN" DOCKED AT BREST WITH TEN THOUSAND MEN ABOARD; FOUR THOUSAND OF THEM HAD THE FLU..

DON'T YOU HAVE ANY COMIC BOOKS?

SCHULZ

HERE'S THE WORLD WAR I FLYING ACE CONFINED TO BED WITH THE TERRIBLE FLU OF 1918...

© 1986 United Feature Syndicate, Inc.

THE BEAUTIFUL FRENCH WAITRESS FROM A NEARBY CAFE HAS BEEN TAKING CARE OF ME...

BONJOUR, MONSIEUR.. I HAVE FOR YOU A PIECE OF MAIL...

2-17

HOW NICE... A "GET WELL" CARD FROM THE RED BARON!

SCHULZ

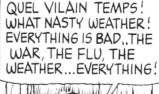

BONJOUR, MADEMOISELLE! QUE DIT-ON DE NOUVEAU?

WHAT'S THE NEWS? RIEN DE NOUVEAU... NOTHING NEW..

2-18

© 1986 United Feature Syndicate, Inc.

QUEL VILAIN TEMPS! WHAT NASTY WEATHER! EVERYTHING IS BAD..THE WAR, THE FLU, THE WEATHER...EVERYTHING!

BLAME IT ON THE ATTORNEYS!

SCHULZ

MONSIEUR! GOOD NEWS! GOOD NEWS!

PRESIDENT WILSON SAID THE ARMISTICE WAS SIGNED THIS MORNING!

THE WAR IS OVER!!

WHEN MY GRANDCHILDREN ASK ME WHAT I DID IN THE WAR, I'LL HAVE TO SAY, "I HAD THE FLU!"

OKAY, I'LL TELL HER

MARCIE WON'T BE IN SCHOOL TODAY, MA'AM... SHE HAS THE FLU...

SHE SAID SHE GOT IT IN FRANCE WHILE TAKING CARE OF A WORLD WAR I FLYING ACE...

YES, MA'AM... SHE'S WEIRD..

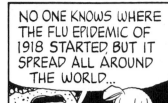

Panel 1: NO ONE KNOWS WHERE THE FLU EPIDEMIC OF 1918 STARTED, BUT IT SPREAD ALL AROUND THE WORLD...

Panel 2: BEFORE IT ENDED IN 1919, TWENTY MILLION PEOPLE HAD DIED...

Panel 3: ASK THE WORLD WAR I FLYING ACE.. HE WAS THERE...

Panel 4: I DON'T GIVE INTERVIEWS!

2-21

© 1986 United Feature Syndicate, Inc.

Panel 5: THEY DID IT AGAIN!

© 1986 United Feature Syndicate, Inc.

Panel 6: BOY, THAT MAKES ME MAD!

Panel 7: THEY PLAY A SONG ON THE RADIO, BUT THEY DON'T TELL YOU WHAT IT WAS!

2-22

Panel 8: THAT WAS THE NATIONAL ANTHEM!

WHAT'S "LL"?

LOUIS L'AMOUR! HE WRITES ALL THOSE WESTERNS..

THAT'S PRETTY NEAT HAVING YOUR INITIALS ON AN ELEVATOR BUTTON!

I DON'T THINK "LL" MEANS LOUIS L'AMOUR.. I THINK IT MEANS "LOWER LOBBY"

REALLY? WHAT DID HE WRITE?

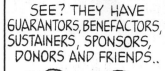
LOOK AT THIS LIST OF PEOPLE WHO SUPPORT THE SYMPHONY, SIR...

SEE? THEY HAVE GUARANTORS, BENEFACTORS, SUSTAINERS, SPONSORS, DONORS AND FRIENDS..

2-27

WHERE DO WE FIT IN?

© 1986 United Feature Syndicate, Inc.

WE'RE THE LISTENERS!

I HOPE THIS CONCERT DOESN'T LAST TOO LONG

WHEN DO YOU THINK IT'LL BE OVER?

© 1986 United Feature Syndicate, Inc.

2-28

WHEN THEY PLAY THE LAST NOTE

THANKS, MARCIE!

ARE YOU ENJOYING THE CONCERT, SIR?

SORT OF...THIS IS A LONG PIECE, ISN'T IT?

© 1986 United Feature Syndicate, Inc.

2-4

YOU HAVE TO CONCENTRATE ON THE MUSIC, AND NOT LET YOUR MIND WANDER..

I THINK MAYBE I'LL HAVE FRENCH TOAST FOR BREAKFAST TOMORROW...

THIS IS MY REPORT ON THE CONCERT WE WENT TO YESTERDAY..

THE MUSIC WAS NICE, AND WE ALL HAD A GOOD TIME..

© 1986 United Feature Syndicate, Inc.

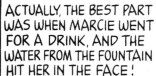
ACTUALLY, THE BEST PART WAS WHEN MARCIE WENT FOR A DRINK, AND THE WATER FROM THE FOUNTAIN HIT HER IN THE FACE!

2-5

YOU'RE WEIRD, SIR!

GOOD AFTERNOON, SIR.. I'M DOING AN ARTICLE FOR OUR SCHOOL PAPER...

HIGH SALARIES AMONG BASEBALL PLAYERS SEEM TO BOTHER SOME PEOPLE.. DOES THIS AFFECT YOU?

3-1

DEFINITELY!

MY TEAM CHARGES ME WAY TOO MUCH TO LET ME PLAY!

© 1986 United Feature Syndicate, Inc.

OKAY, TEAM.. WE LOST, BUT LET'S BE GOOD SPORTS ABOUT IT...

LET'S GIVE OUR OPPONENTS A GOOD OLD-FASHIONED "HIP, HIP, HURRAY!"

3-3

© 1986 United Feature Syndicate, Inc.

I HATE LOSING!

I'LL "HIP, HIP," BUT I WON'T "HURRAY!"

THEY SAY THAT MY GREAT-GRANDFATHER WAS ALWAYS EARLY... NO MATTER WHERE HE WENT, HE WAS ALWAYS EARLY...

IF HE WENT TO A BALL GAME OR TO A SHOW, HE ALWAYS GOT THERE EARLY, AND WAS ALWAYS THE FIRST ONE TO LEAVE...

DID HE LIVE TO A RIPE OLD AGE?

3-4

NO, HE LEFT EARLY!

SO HERE I AM RIDING ON THE BACK OF MY MOM'S BICYCLE...

I LIKE MY NEW HELMET

MOM'S BECOME VERY SAFETY CONSCIOUS...

3-5

BABY ON BIKE

PEANUTS
featuring
"Good ol' Charlie Brown"
by Schulz

WHAT'S GOING ON?

IT'S A SPECIAL INSTRUMENT TO MEASURE THE SPEED OF YOUR FASTBALL, CHARLIE BROWN...

REALLY? I'VE ALWAYS WONDERED HOW FAST I THROW

WE'RE ALL SET.. PITCH IT WHEN YOU'RE READY..

THIS'LL BE GREAT.. WHEN OTHER TEAMS HEAR THAT MY FASTBALL HAS BEEN OFFICIALLY TIMED, THEY'LL BE SCARED TO DEATH...

3-2

© 1986 United Feature Syndicate, Inc.

DID YOU GET IT? DO YOU WANT ME TO THROW ANOTHER ONE?

THAT'S ALL RIGHT.. I THINK WE GOT IT...

A D-MINUS... AAUGHH!!

A B-PLUS... AAUGHH!!

THAT PROVES IT, MA'AM..

3-6

WE ALL HAVE DIFFERENT THRESHOLDS OF PAIN!

© 1986 United Feature Syndicate, Inc.

I FEEL KIND OF ACHY TODAY

© 1986 United Feature Syndicate, Inc.

3-7

MAYBE YOUR BODY IS TRYING TO TELL YOU SOMETHING

WE'D ALL BE A LOT HEALTHIER IF WE LISTENED TO OUR BODIES..

" I MEAN, AFTER ALL, NONE OF US IS GETTING ANY YOUNGER, AND I GET TIRED, TOO, YOU KNOW, AND YET WHERE IS ALL THE FUN, AND WHO IS TO SAY, AND WHY, AND.."

3-10

© 1986 United Feature Syndicate, Inc.

THIS PROGRAM WAS BROUGHT TO YOU AS A PUBLIC SERVICE..

CONSULT YOUR PAPER FOR A COMPLETE LISTING OF FUTURE PROGRAMS

AND NOW FOR A COMMUNITY REMINDER...

3-11

© 1986 United Feature Syndicate, Inc.

WAKE UP!

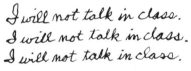

WHAT IF A GIRL GOT SO MAD BECAUSE SHE HAD TO WRITE, "I WILL NOT TALK IN CLASS" A HUNDRED TIMES THAT SHE NEVER SAID ANOTHER WORD FOR THE REST OF HER LIFE?

3-9

SO THEN WHAT IF HER PARENTS SUED HER TEACHER, THE PRINCIPAL, THE BOARD OF EDUCATION, THE STATE SUPERINTENDENT AND THE FEDERAL GOVERNMENT?

I will not talk in class.
I will not talk in class.
I will not talk in class.

WELL, I FINISHED... YOU'RE LUCKY...

WHY AM I LUCKY?

THEY WERE GOING TO SUE YOU, TOO!

LET ME GO OVER THIS AGAIN..

3-12

YOU LIKE YOUR SUPPER IN THE RED DISH AND YOUR DRINKING WATER IN THE YELLOW DISH...

AND THE CHOCOLATE CHIP COOKIES IN THE BLUE DISH!

© 1986 United Feature Syndicate, Inc.

IF I HAD A BLUE DISH

It was a dark and stormy night.

3-13

Suddenly, a shot rang out!

© 1986 United Feature Syndicate, Inc.

Then another! And another! And then some more.

Shots, that is.

PEANUTS featuring "Good ol' CharlieBrown" by SCHULZ

WHERE ARE YOU GOING, MARCIE?

TO WATCH CHARLES FLY A KITE..IT'S SOMETHING I'VE ALWAYS WANTED TO SEE...

WELL, WHAT DO YOU THINK?

IT WAS AN EXPERIENCE

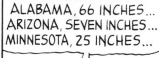

Panel 1: SEE, THIS TELLS YOU HOW MUCH RAIN EACH PLACE GETS IN A YEAR..

Panel 2: ALABAMA, 66 INCHES... ARIZONA, SEVEN INCHES... MINNESOTA, 25 INCHES...

Panel 3: MOUNT WAIALEALE, ON HAWAII, IS THE RAINIEST.. IT GETS 460 INCHES OF RAIN A YEAR...

3-17

Panel 4: WHOSE IDEA WAS THAT?

Panel 5: IS THAT ALL YOU'RE HAVING FOR LUNCH, SIR? JUST FRENCH FRIES?

Panel 6: I HAVE A THEORY THAT EATING TOO MANY FRENCH FRIES CAUSES MEMORY LOSS AND PERSONALITY ALTERATIONS...

Panel 7: 3-18

I DOUBT IT, MARCIE..

Panel 8: IF THEY DID, THERE'D BE A WARNING ON THE SIDE OF EACH ONE..

YOU'RE WEIRD, SIR..

© 1986 United Feature Syndicate, Inc.

GRAMPA SAYS THIS IS THE TIME OF YEAR WHEN KIDS USED TO SHOOT MARBLES

HE SAYS YOU JUST DON'T SEE KIDS DOING THAT ANYMORE

© 1986 United Feature Syndicate, Inc.

OF COURSE NOT..

3/19

WHY WOULD ANYONE WANT TO SHOOT A MARBLE?

THIS IS HOW YOU SHOOT A MARBLE..

YOU PUT IT BETWEEN YOUR SECOND FINGER AND YOUR THUMB WITH THE TIP OF YOUR FOREFINGER UNDERNEATH..

3-20

I CAN THINK OF AN EASIER WAY...

© 1986 United Feature Syndicate, Inc.

KICK IT!!!

SCHULZ

PEANUTS
featuring
"*Good ol'
CharlieBrown*"
by SCHULZ

"WHO DID WHAT, WHERE, WHEN AND WHY?" GOOD GRIEF!

THIS IS THE HARDEST TEST I'VE EVER SEEN

THE FIRST QUESTION GAVE ME A HEADACHE..

THE SECOND QUESTION MADE MY CHEST HURT...

OUCH!

MOLLY VOLLEY IS ON THE PHONE

SHE WANTS YOU TO BE HER PARTNER IN THE SPRING MIXED DOUBLES TENNIS TOURNAMENT

3-24

© 1986 United Feature Syndicate, Inc.

SHE'S THE ONE WITH THE FAT FACE, THE FAT BODY AND THE FAT LEGS...

SCHULZ

SHE WANTS TO KNOW IF YOU REMEMBER HER..

VAGUELY..

OKAY, PARTNER, HERE'S THE WAY IT'S GOING TO BE...

IF WE WIN, I TAKE THE CREDIT...

3-25

IF WE LOSE, YOU TAKE THE BLAME!

© 1986 United Feature Syndicate, Inc.

WHO GETS THE CHOCOLATE CHIP COOKIES?

 YOU THOUGHT I'D FORGET THE CHOCOLATE CHIP COOKIES, DIDN'T YOU?

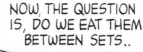 NOW, THE QUESTION IS, DO WE EAT THEM BETWEEN SETS..

3-26

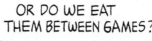 OR DO WE EAT THEM BETWEEN GAMES?

 HOW ABOUT BETWEEN POINTS?

© 1986 United Feature Syndicate, Inc.

 HEY, PARTNER..

 HOW DO YOU EXPECT TO PLAY TENNIS AND EAT COOKIES AT THE SAME TIME?!

3-27

 I CAN HANDLE THAT...

© 1986 United Feature Syndicate, Inc.

 THE HARD PART IS RECEIVING SERVE WHILE DUNKING A COOKIE IN A GLASS OF MILK...

PEANUTS
featuring
"Good ol' Charlie Brown"
by Schulz

?

OH, NO!

LOOK AT THE BUMP ON THE BACK OF MY HAND..

YOU HAVE A "GANGLION"

YOU KNOW HOW THEY SAY TO CURE IT? YOU HAVE SOMEONE HIT IT WITH A BIBLE!

© 1986 United Feature Syndicate, Inc.

WITH A WHAT?

I WONDER WHICH TRANSLATION WOULD WORK BEST...

I SUPPOSE THEY USED THE "KING JAMES" IN THE OLD DAYS..THE "REVISED STANDARD" SHOULD WORK JUST AS WELL

MAYBE THE "TYNDALE" OR THE "DOUAY"...OR MAYBE WE SHOULD USE THE "MOFFATT"...

WHAT ARE YOU MUMBLING ABOUT? HERE, HIT IT WITH THIS...

3-30

BONK!

WHAT DO YOU THINK YOU'RE DOING? YOU WERE SUPPOSED TO HIT MY HAND!

SORRY.. YOU MOVED

I'M GONNA DO WHAT I SHOULD HAVE DONE! I'M GONNA CALL OUR DOCTOR!

WAIT A MINUTE! THIS WAS "A TALE OF TWO CITIES"!!

SCHULZ

SO HERE I AM AGAIN RIDING ON THE BACK OF MOM'S BICYCLE..

I THINK I'LL SUGGEST THAT I DO THE STEERING TODAY AND LET MOM RIDE ON THE BACK...

NO, MAYBE NOT..

MANAGEMENT ISN'T MUCH FOR TAKING SUGGESTIONS

3-31

© 1986 United Feature Syndicate, Inc.

YOU'RE ALWAYS CRITICIZING MY LUNCHES...

WELL, TAKE A LOOK AT WHAT I HAVE TODAY.. TWO SANDWICHES, COTTAGE CHEESE AND AN APPLE...

NO NAPKIN RINGS!

HA HA HA HA HA HA!

YOU'RE WEIRD, MARCIE

4-1

© 1986 United Feature Syndicate, Inc.

I HAVE TO WRITE A REPORT FOR SCHOOL ON THE SECRET OF LIFE...

CAN YOU GIVE ME SOME SUGGESTIONS?

4-2

TURN OFF APPLIANCES WHEN NOT IN USE, FORM CAR POOLS AND DEFROST FOODS BEFORE COOKING

I'LL GO ASK SOMEONE ELSE

I AGREE..

YES, MA'AM..MARCIE AND I WERE JUST TALKING ABOUT YOU

4-3

WE'VE DECIDED THAT YOU'RE THE BEST TEACHER IN THIS WHOLE SCHOOL...

POUND FOR POUND, THAT IS!

I ALWAYS FEEL SO GUILTY..

BUT WHY SHOULD I? WHY CAN'T I JUST TAKE OFF WITHOUT SAYING ANYTHING?

4-4

NO, I ALWAYS FEEL GUILTY, AND I ALWAYS ASK...

© 1986 United Feature Syndicate, Inc.

I'M GOING INTO TOWN.. DO YOU WANT ME TO BRING YOU ANYTHING?

© 1986 United Feature Syndicate, Inc.

4-5

NOW WHAT?

HEY, MANAGER, REMEMBER OUR LAST GAME WHEN YOU WALKED SO MANY BATTERS I ALMOST FELL ASLEEP OUT IN RIGHT FIELD?

WELL, DON'T WORRY ABOUT IT...TODAY I'M READY!

DON'T LOOK NOW, BUT SOME PEOPLE ARE WATCHING YOU..

I THINK THEY'RE BIRD WATCHERS...

4-7 © 1986 United Feature Syndicate, Inc.

HOW EMBARRASSING!

DO YOU KNOW WHY I'M LIMPING?

WHEN I WAS FIXING YOUR DINNER, I DROPPED THE CAN OF DOG FOOD ON MY FOOT!

I ALSO CUT MY FINGER ON THE CAN OPENER...

THIS WOULD BE A BAD TIME TO ASK FOR AN AFTER DINNER MINT

© 1986 United Feature Syndicate, Inc. 4-8

PEANUTS featuring "Good ol' Charlie Brown" by SCHULZ

Game today

HI, CHUCK! YOU'VE BEEN OVER HERE, AND WATCHED SOME OF OUR GAMES, HAVEN'T YOU?

4-6

SURE, I'M ONE OF YOUR BIGGEST FANS.. YOU HAVE A GREAT TEAM..

WELL, GOOD! YOU SHOULD COME OVER TODAY BECAUSE IT'S "FAN APPRECIATION DAY"

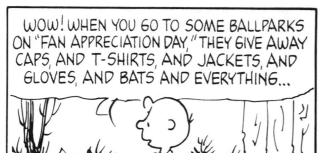

WOW! WHEN YOU GO TO SOME BALLPARKS ON "FAN APPRECIATION DAY," THEY GIVE AWAY CAPS, AND T-SHIRTS, AND JACKETS, AND GLOVES, AND BATS AND EVERYTHING...

HI, FAN!

WE APPRECIATE YOU!! ?!

YOU MEAN THAT'S IT?

WE HAVE A LOW BUDGET, CHUCK!

PARTLY CLOUDY AND COOLER..

4-9

AFTERNOON SUNNY.. CLEARING TONIGHT

© 1986 United Feature Syndicate, Inc.

AND NOW, A COMMUNITY REMINDER..

DON'T REMIND ME!

IF YOU SINK THIS PUTT, YOU'LL WIN THE TOURNAMENT..

4-10

YOU CAN DO IT..

© 1986 United Feature Syndicate, Inc.

I'M NOT SO SURE..

IT'S HARD TO PUTT WHEN YOU'RE BLEEDING INTERNALLY!

I WAS WATCHING THIS MOVIE, SEE, WHERE THESE GUYS ARE CHASING SOME OTHER GUYS IN A CAR..

4-11

AS THEY TEAR AROUND A CORNER, THEY KNOCK OVER A FRUIT STAND, AND ORANGES FLY ALL OVER!

THEN, BOTH CARS GO ROARING OFF DOWN THE ROAD!

NO ONE EVER GOES BACK TO HELP PICK UP THE ORANGES..

4-12

HERE'S THE WORLD FAMOUS SERGEANT OF THE FOREIGN LEGION LEADING HIS TROOPS TO RETAKE FORT ZINDERNEUF

4-14

QUICKLY THEY MOVE THE CANNON INTO POSITION...

SLOWLY THEY MOVE THE CANNON INTO POSITION...

© 1986 United Feature Syndicate, Inc.

THEY DECIDE IT LOOKS PRETTY GOOD RIGHT WHERE IT IS...

SCHULZ

READY, MEN? THIS IS IT!

BOOM!

GOOD GRIEF!

4-15 © 1986 United Feature Syndicate, Inc.

WHAT HAVE WE DONE TO FORT ZINDERNEUF?!

SEND YOU MONEY? I DON'T HAVE ANY MONEY! I'M JUST A LITTLE KID! WHERE WOULD I GET MONEY?!

TELL YOU WHAT I'LL DO... AFTER I FINISH COLLEGE AND GET A JOB, I'LL TRY TO SEND YOU A LITTLE, OKAY?

4-21 © 1986 United Feature Syndicate, Inc.

STOP ASKING ME!!!

I'M THE BIG SISTER AND YOU'RE THE LITTLE BROTHER! THAT'S THE WAY IT'S ALWAYS GOING TO BE!

IT'S GOING TO BE THAT WAY TODAY, TOMORROW, NEXT WEEK AND FOREVER!

SIGH

HA! I KNEW THAT'D GET A RISE OUT OF YOU!

PEANUTS
featuring
"Good ol' CharlieBrown"
by SCHULZ

4-20

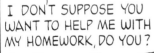

4-25

© 1986 United Feature Syndicate, Inc.

HI!

DO YOU COME HERE OFTEN?

4-26

© 1986 United Feature Syndicate, Inc.

I FALL IN LOVE TOO EASY..

PEANUTS
featuring
"Good ol' Charlie Brown"
by SCHULZ

!

OH, NO!

HEY LUCY.. I HEAR YOU'VE BEEN ELECTED "QUEEN OF THE MAY"

THAT'S RIGHT

4-28
© 1986 United Feature Syndicate, Inc.

CONGRATULATIONS!

THANK YOU

HERE, MARCIE.. READ IT, AND SEE IF I'M NOT RIGHT...

© 1986 United Feature Syndicate, Inc.

"MAY QUEEN..."

4-29

"A GIRL CHOSEN TO BE QUEEN OF THE MERRYMAKERS ON MAY DAY AND CROWNED WITH FLOWERS"

I VOLUNTEER!

SCHULZ

YES, MA'AM, I VOLUNTEER TO BE "QUEEN OF THE MAY"

I CAN'T VOLUNTEER?

4-30

SHE'S RIGHT, SIR...YOU HAVE TO BE CHOSEN...

© 1986 United Feature Syndicate, Inc.

OKAY, I CHOOSE **ME**!!

HEY, CHUCK, GUESS WHAT...I'M RUNNING FOR "QUEEN OF THE MAY" AT OUR SCHOOL!

5-1

THAT'S INTERESTING... LUCY HAS ALREADY BEEN CHOSEN AT OUR SCHOOL

YOUR SCHOOL HAS PRETTY LOW STANDARDS, HUH, CHUCK?

© 1986 United Feature Syndicate, Inc.

SHE SAYS, "CONGRATULATIONS"

GREAT NEWS, SIR! YOU'VE BEEN SELECTED TO BE OUR "QUEEN OF THE MAY"!
I KNEW IT! I KNEW I'D BE CHOSEN! JUST WAIT 'TIL THEY SEE ME LEAD THE DANCE AROUND THE MAYPOLE..
5-2
THEY CANCELED THE MAYPOLE DANCE, SIR...
OUR SCHOOL LOST ITS LIABILITY INSURANCE!
SCHULZ
© 1986 United Feature Syndicate, Inc.

THEY CANCELED OUR MAYPOLE DANCE BECAUSE OUR SCHOOL DOESN'T HAVE LIABILITY INSURANCE?
THAT'S RIDICULOUS!
© 1986 United Feature Syndicate, Inc.
WHO WOULD BE CLUMSY ENOUGH TO GET TANGLED AROUND A MAYPOLE?
5-3
SCHULZ

BONK! ①

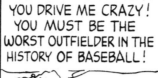

YOU DRIVE ME CRAZY! YOU MUST BE THE WORST OUTFIELDER IN THE HISTORY OF BASEBALL!

5-6

© 1986 United Feature Syndicate, Inc.

THAT'S NOT VERY ENCOURAGING!!!

I THINK YOU EXPECT TOO MUCH OF YOUR PLAYERS, CHARLIE BROWN..

5-7

AFTER ALL, WE'RE NOT PROFESSIONALS! WE'RE ONLY....

ONLY WHAT?

© 1986 United Feature Syndicate, Inc.

WHAT'S BELOW AMATEUR?

PEANUTS
featuring
"Good ol' Charlie Brown"
by Schulz

I NEVER REALIZED WE HAD SO MUCH INFLUENCE..

5-5

MY GRANDFATHER WASHES HIS HAIR EVERY DAY...

HE ALSO USES A CONDITIONER AND BRUSHES IT A LOT

5-8

THAT TAKES REAL DEDICATION

UH HUH

HIS HAIR'S IN BETTER SHAPE THAN HE IS!

DOES EVERYONE HAVE HIS CANTEEN FILLED?

© 1986 United Feature Syndicate, Inc.   5-12

YOU CAN'T GO ON A LONG HIKE LIKE THIS WITHOUT WATER

ALWAYS REMEMBER... WATER IS OUR FRIEND..

THANKS, FRIEND

A GOOD OUTDOORS PERSON LEARNS TO PREDICT THE WEATHER

CAN ANYONE TELL ME WHAT THE WEATHER IS GOING TO BE TODAY?

"FAIR AND WARMER".. AMAZING! TELL US HOW YOU KNEW THAT...

© 1986 United Feature Syndicate, Inc.   5-13

I THINK IT'S A SIN TO BE BORED

JUST LOOK AT THE WORLD AROUND YOU..

JUST THINK OF ALL THE WONDERFUL THINGS OUT THERE FOR US TO SEE...

WELL, YES, IF THAT ROCK WASN'T IN THE WAY..

5-14

   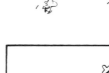 

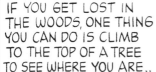

IF YOU GET LOST IN THE WOODS, ONE THING YOU CAN DO IS CLIMB TO THE TOP OF A TREE TO SEE WHERE YOU ARE..

CONRAD WILL NOW DEMONSTRATE FOR US HOW THIS IS DONE...

5-15   © 1986 United Feature Syndicate,Inc.

SEE THAT MOUNTAIN? WE'RE GOING TO THE TOP!

OF COURSE, THIS COULD BE JUST A LITTLE BIT DANGEROUS..

5-16

THEREFORE, I WANT YOU TO TIE THIS ROPE AROUND YOUR WAISTS, OKAY?

ADMIT IT, YOU ALL FEEL MORE SECURE NOW, DON'T YOU?

WE DID IT! WE MADE IT TO THE TOP!

WHAT AN EXPERIENCE!

5-17

I'M SO EXCITED I FEEL LIKE YODELING!

OKAY, FORGET THE YODELING..

PEANUTS featuring "Good ol' Charlie Brown" by Schulz

HEY, MANAGER..

YOU KNOW WHAT WE OUGHT TO DO TO WIN? WE OUGHT TO PRAY..

PRAY?! WOULD THAT BE FAIR?

WHY NOT? I PRAY ALL THE TIME OUT THERE IN RIGHT FIELD... I PRAY THEY WON'T HIT THE BALL TO ME

Dear Sweetheart,

© 1986 United Feature Syndicate, Inc.

THAT'S TOO IMPERSONAL

I THINK YOU SHOULD CALL HER SOMETHING MORE ENDEARING...

5-21

Dear Angel Food Cake With Seven Minute Frosting,

SUMMER MUST BE NEAR..

© 1986 United Feature Syndicate, Inc.

THE EVENINGS ARE WARM...

BIRDS ARE SITTING IN FRONT OF THEIR NESTS..

5-22

..IN THEIR LITTLE ROCKING CHAIRS..

5-23

SORRY, MA'AM.. I JUST SORT OF DOZED OFF.. I APOLOGIZE...

SEE? I HANG MY HEAD IN SHAME...

© 1986 United Feature Syndicate, Inc.

5-24

HE SAID HE HAD SOMETHING TO TELL ME..HERE HE COMES..

AND LOOK WHAT HE'S BRINGING WITH HIM..

NOW I KNOW IT'S GOING TO BE ONE OF HIS LONG STORIES..

© 1986 United Feature Syndicate, Inc.

✳SIGH✳

PEANUTS featuring "Good ol' Charlie Brown" by SCHULZ

YES, MA'AM.. I'M READY

THIS IS MY SCIENCE PROJECT..

"TOAST ON A STICK!"

© 1986 United Feature Syndicate, Inc.

5-25

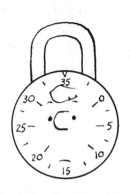

PEANUTS
featuring "Good ol' Charlie Brown"
by SCHULZ

WHAT'S THIS?

THESE ARE OUR NEW SAFETY DESKS, CHARLIE BROWN

SAFETY DESKS?

HOW DID YOU DO ON YOUR FINAL REPORT CARD, SIR?

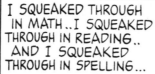

I SQUEAKED THROUGH IN MATH..I SQUEAKED THROUGH IN READING.. AND I SQUEAKED THROUGH IN SPELLING...

6-6

I CAN'T BELIEVE IT!

SQUEAK! SQUEAK! SQUEAK!

DID BEETHOVEN EVER TEACH KINDERGARTEN? PROBABLY NOT...

© 1986 United Feature Syndicate, Inc.

PROBABLY DIDN'T LIKE KIDS...PROBABLY HATED KIDS..PROBABLY FORGOT THAT HE WAS A KID ONCE HIMSELF...

BONK!

WAS BEETHOVEN EVER A KID?

6-7

OKAY, PARTNER, NOW!

6-8

I DON'T HAVE ANY SHOELACES.. I DON'T EVEN HAVE ANY SHOES!

NOW, PARTNER! I SAID, "NOW!"

© 1986 United Feature Syndicate, Inc.

IT HURTS WHEN YOU TIE YOUR TOES TOGETHER!

Panel 1: HI! MY NAME IS LINUS.. MAY I SIT WITH YOU AND EAT LUNCH?

© 1986 United Feature Syndicate, Inc.

Panel 2: I DON'T KNOW..WHEN WERE YOU BORN?

I WAS BORN IN OCTOBER..

6-9

Panel 3: I WAS BORN IN DECEMBER

Panel 4: AREN'T YOU KIND OF OLD FOR ME?

SCHULZ

Panel 5: I CAN'T BELIEVE IT! I CAN'T BELIEVE WHAT SHE SAID!

© 1986 United Feature Syndicate, Inc.

Panel 6: I ASKED THIS CUTE LITTLE GIRL IF I COULD SIT AND EAT LUNCH WITH HER..THAT'S ALL I ASKED..

Panel 7: YOU KNOW WHAT SHE SAID? SHE SAID, "AREN'T YOU KIND OF OLD FOR ME?" I COULDN'T BELIEVE IT!!

6-10

Panel 8: YOU ARE LOOKING KIND OF OLD..

SCHULZ

 AREN'T YOU THE GIRL I SAW ON THE PLAYGROUND YESTERDAY? WHAT ARE YOU DOING HERE?

I'M NOT SUPPOSED TO CROSS THE STREET ALONE

NO PROBLEM.. I'LL GO WITH YOU... MY PLEASURE..

6-11

I TOLD YOU MY NAME IS LINUS, DIDN'T I? IT'S A PLEASURE JUST TO BE WALKING WITH YOU...

THANKS, MISTER

MISTER?

© 1986 United Feature Syndicate, Inc.

I WALKED ACROSS THE STREET WITH HER... THAT'S ALL I DID!

© 1986 United Feature Syndicate, Inc.

YOU KNOW WHAT SHE SAID? SHE SAID, "THANKS, MISTER"

6-12

I'M ONLY TWO MONTHS OLDER THAN SHE IS, AND SHE CALLS ME "MISTER"!!

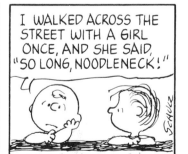

I WALKED ACROSS THE STREET WITH A GIRL ONCE, AND SHE SAID, "SO LONG, NOODLENECK!"

Panel 1: WELL, HI! FANCY MEETING YOU HERE... REMEMBER ME? LINUS VAN PELT?

Panel 2: I'LL HAVE MINT CHOCOLATE CHIP, PLEASE

Panel 3: I'LL HAVE THE SAME, PLEASE... YOU LIKE MINT CHOCOLATE CHIP? I'M SURPRISED...

6-13

Panel 4: MOST OLDER PEOPLE LIKE VANILLA!

© 1986 United Feature Syndicate, Inc.

Panel 5: SO I ORDERED MINT CHOCOLATE CHIP JUST LIKE SHE DID, AND SHE SAID SHE WAS SURPRISED...

Panel 6: SHE SAYS, "MOST OLDER PEOPLE ORDER VANILLA!" WHAT SHE REALLY MEANT WAS SHE THINKS I'M DULL AND BORING!

6-14 © 1986 United Feature Syndicate, Inc.

Panel 8: I'VE ALWAYS LIKED VANILLA

EXCUSE ME..MAYBE I HAVE NO RIGHT TO ASK YOU THIS, BUT...

DIDN'T I SEE YOU YESTERDAY WITH ANOTHER KID WHO MUST BE AT LEAST A YEAR OLDER THAN YOU?

I'M ONLY TWO MONTHS OLDER THAN YOU..WHY IS HIS AGE OKAY BUT MINE ISN'T?

© 1986 United Feature Syndicate, Inc.

6-16

THERE'S OLDER, AND THEN THERE'S OLDER!

MAY I SPEAK TO YOU ABOUT MY FRIEND HERE?

I THINK YOU'RE WRONG ABOUT HIS BEING TOO OLD FOR YOU..

IN MANY WAYS, HE'S STILL QUITE YOUNG..

© 1986 United Feature Syndicate, Inc.

6-17

I MEAN, YOU SHOULD SEE HIM WITH HIS BLANKET..

AAUGH!

HERE I AM TRYING TO CONVINCE THIS GIRL I'M NOT TOO OLD FOR HER, AND YOU TELL HER THAT I STILL HAVE A BLANKET!

6-18

WHAT CAN I SAY? DON'T SAY ANYTHING!

© 1986 United Feature Syndicate, Inc.

I'M GOOD AT THAT..

THAT WAS GREAT! THAT WAS JUST GREAT!!

RIGHT LEG..LEFT LEG..RIGHT LEG..LEFT LEG..

SWING YOUR ARMS.. LIFT YOUR KNEES..

NOW, JUST RELAX YOUR BREATHING, AND LET ALL THE TENSION GO OUT OF YOUR BODY...

6-19   © 1986 United Feature Syndicate, Inc.

FEAR CAN TAKE CONTROL OF OUR VERY LIVES!

FEAR OF POVERTY.. FEAR OF ILLNESS...

IF YOU WERE TO ASK ME WHAT MY GREATEST FEAR IS, DO YOU KNOW WHAT I'D SAY?

CANCELLATION!

6-20

© 1986 United Feature Syndicate, Inc.

LONG HAIR IS OUT, YOU KNOW

SHORT HAIR IS IN..

© 1986 United Feature Syndicate, Inc.   6-21

ON THE OTHER HAND, MAYBE I WAS WRONG

PEANUTS

featuring

"Good ol' Charlie Brown"

by Schulz

June 15

Dear Dad,
Just a few lines to wish you a happy Father's Day.

I know you worry about me living alone out here on the desert, but I don't want you to worry about me.

Actually, some nice things have been happening...

6-23

I WONDER IF I SNORED LAST NIGHT..

I DID?

HEY, MANAGER, IT'S TOO HOT OUT HERE!

YESTERDAY YOU SAID IT WAS TOO COLD! MAKE UP YOUR MIND!

6-24

IT'S TOO NICE OUT HERE!

FALLING ROCK

6-25

© 1986 United Feature Syndicate, Inc.

NEXT TIME

ALL RIGHT, THAT DOES IT!

© 1986 United Feature Syndicate, Inc.

JUST ANSWER ME THIS ONE QUESTION..

I THINK I HAVE A RIGHT TO KNOW

6-26

WHAT'S A ZAMBONI DOING ON A BASEBALL FIELD?

IN CASE YOU'RE INTERESTED, THERE'S A ZAMBONI HEADED YOUR WAY!

WHAT'S A ZAMBONI?

© 1986 United Feature Syndicate, Inc.

A ZAMBONI IS THE MACHINE THAT RESURFACES THE ICE BETWEEN PERIODS AT A HOCKEY GAME...

6-27

I'M TOO YOUNG TO BE RESURFACED!

?

BEEP BEEP

© 1986 United Feature Syndicate, Inc.   6-28

WHY CAN'T I HAVE A NORMAL GROUNDSKEEPER LIKE EVERYONE ELSE?

WELCOME TO THE FIRST MEETING OF OUR POLKA CLUB!

6-30 © 1986 United Feature Syndicate, Inc.

WE'RE ALL HERE TO HAVE A GOOD TIME SO LET'S GET STARTED..

CHOOSE YOUR PARTNERS!

DO YOU COME HERE OFTEN?

HELLO?

NO, I CAN'T... NOT TOMORROW..

YEAH, THE DENTIST..

© 1986 United Feature Syndicate, Inc.

I HAVE TO GO HAVE MY TEETH CRITICIZED!

7-1

LOOK, MARCIE..TWELVE OF THE CHAIRS IN THE ORCHESTRA ARE EMPTY

THIS FIRST PIECE IS FOR A SMALL ORCHESTRA, SIR..

THEY DON'T NEED ALL OF THE PLAYERS

© 1986 United Feature Syndicate, Inc.

7-2

I THOUGHT MAYBE THEY HAD THE FLU..

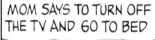
MOM SAYS TO TURN OFF THE TV AND GO TO BED

7-3 © 1986 United Feature Syndicate, Inc.